Frank and Bert

THE ONE WHERE BERT LEARNS TO RIDE A BIKE

Chris Naylor-Ballesteros

nosy crow

Hello, I'm Frank.
This is me and my best friend, Bert.

We'd like to go on a big bike ride,
but there's one little problem.

Bert isn't very good at riding
a bike.

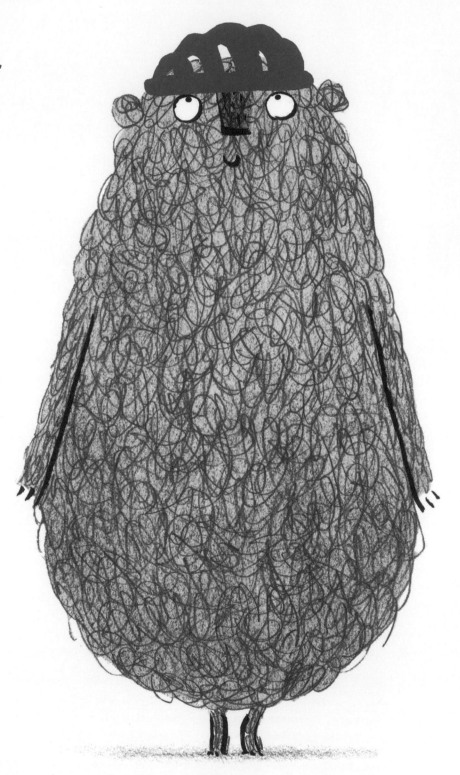

Here's what happens.

It always starts well, but then Bert
wibble-wobbles all over the place,
until . . .

Ouch!

Do you see what I mean?

But today, Bert is **absolutely certain** he can do it.
"Trust me," he says. "I'll be fine!"

I'm not so sure, but Bert **really** wants to prove
he can ride a bike just as well as me.

So off we go!

As usual, it starts well, but then Bert wibble-wobbles all over the place until . . .

Oh no!

Bert! Watch out!

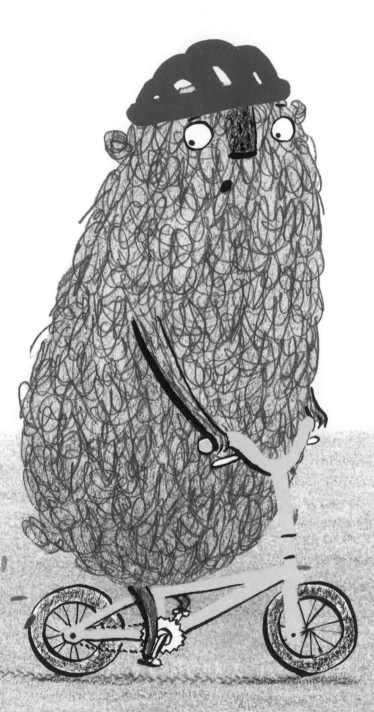

Oh dear.

"Oh, Bert! Never mind," I say, and I tell him not to worry because I have a brilliant plan – I'll hold on to his bike to help him balance while he practises **not** wibble-wobbling.

What could possibly go wrong?

Bert says OK but only if I promise to stay **right behind** him **all** the time.

"I promise," I say.

As usual, it's a good start and . . .

Bert's doing **really well!**

In fact, Bert is doing SO well that I decide to let go –
I'm sure he'll be **completely** fine!

And guess what?

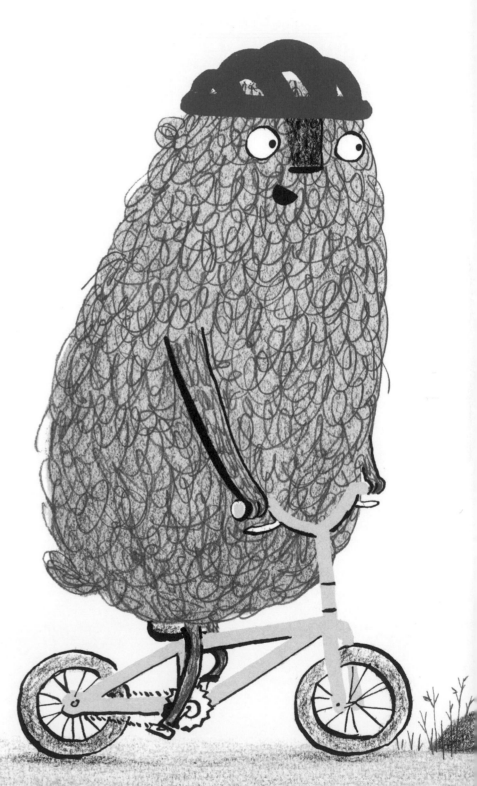

Oops!

Bert is **very** cross. He says I promised to stay **right behind** him but I didn't and I let go and **that's** why he fell off.

I tell him I'm really sorry, but Bert says he **never** wants to ride a bike **ever** again and goes straight home.

Oh dear. I'll have to do something **extra special** to make it up to my best friend.

In fact, I have another idea which might be just the thing . . .

I go to see Bert the next day and show him what I've done.

"Look, Bert! An extra seat on my bike! Now you can sit on the back, and I'll do all the pedalling. It will be great!"

Bert isn't so cross with me now, and he thinks this is quite a good idea.

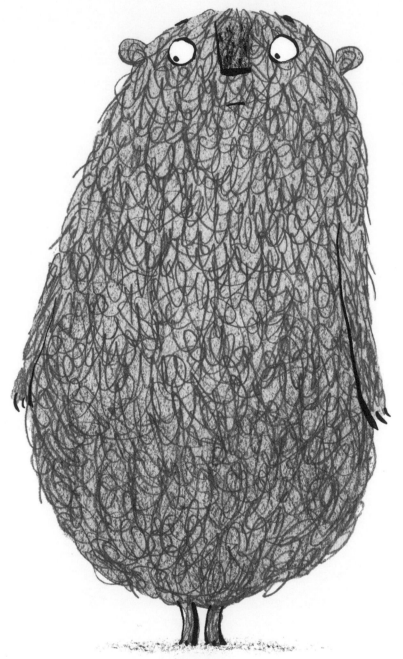

So off we go . . . again!

It's a good start and we're having a great time!
Though Bert is a bit heavier than I thought, and . . .

this hill is . . .

really . . .

quite . . .

steep . . .

and by the time
we get to the top . . .

... I am
completely
exhausted!

My legs have turned to jelly
and I have to lie down.
I'll **never** be able to pedal
us both back home.

"Save yourself, Bert!" I groan.
"Walk home and leave me here . . .
I'll only slow you down!"

But Bert says, "No way! I'll never leave you, Frank!
You get on the back and I'll go at the front . . .
we'll be home in no time!"

Poor Bert – as much as he'd love to help,
this will be a DISASTER!

So I say, "Poor Bert, as much as you'd
love to help, this will be a DISASTER!"

But Bert is **absolutely certain** he can do it.
"Trust me," he says.
"We'll be fine!"

I'm not so sure,
but what can I do?

So . . .
off we go . . .
AGAIN.

And guess what?

BERT DOES IT!

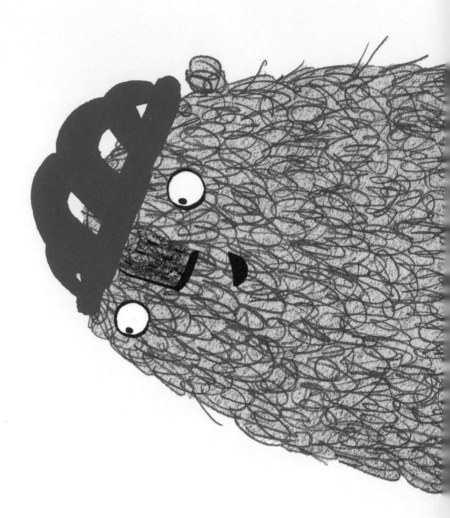

We speed down the hill,

zooming between trees

and jumping over rocks . . .

all the way home!

"Bert!" I say. "That was amazing – you did it!"

Bert gives me a big smile and says, "Of course I did it,
because you were right behind me all the way!"

This is me and my best friend, Bert.

Today we're going on a big bike ride.
Bert is much better at it now and
hardly wibble-wobbles at all.

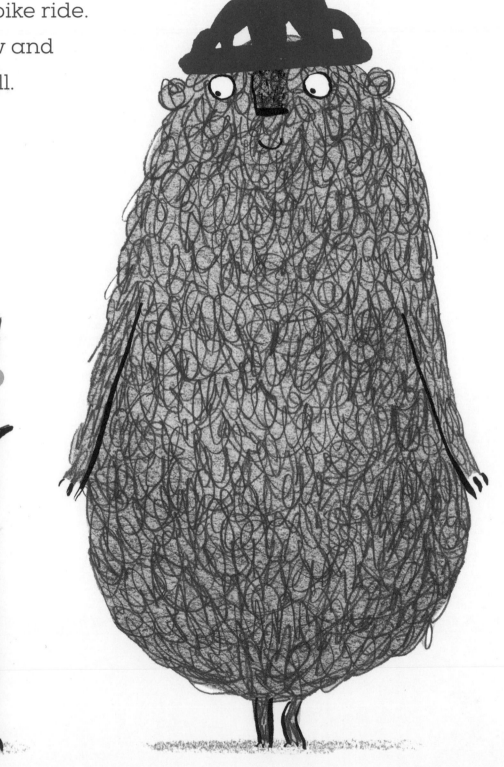

But I always keep an eye on him,
just to make sure he's OK . . .

Oops.